Contents

Cool New Costumes!

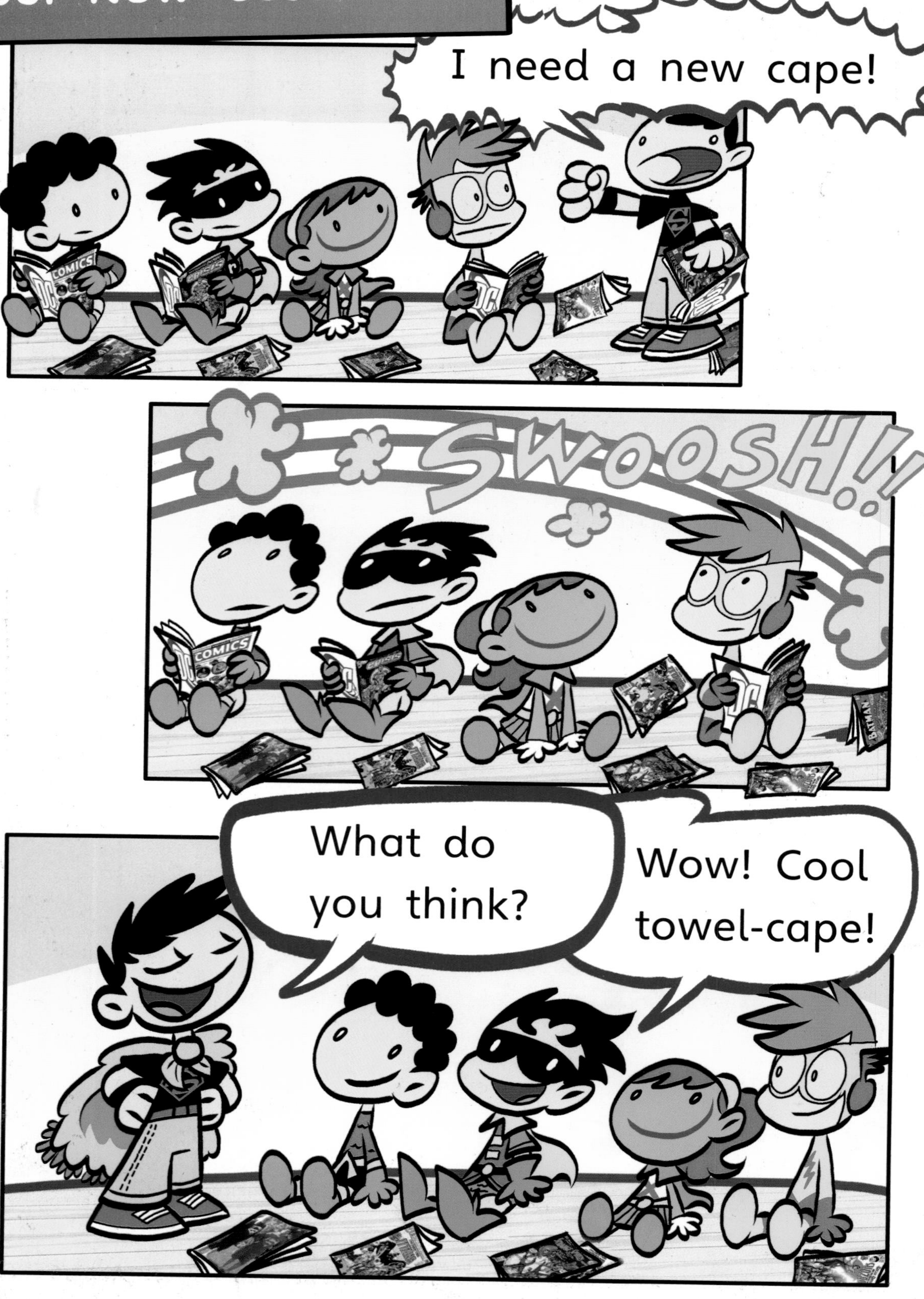

Far away, the hunt for a new costume is on ...

I can put on one of Superman's costumes!

Look out! The mirror is not quite what it seems ...

Too late!

Aha! Superman! How kind of you to visit us in the mirror zone!

But ... I am not Superman!

You cannot fool us. That is Superman's costume!

Er ... big mistake! See you!

5

Batcow called for help ...

Who is Who?

Can you spot eight seashells?

Three days later ...

ZZZZ

ZZZZ

ZZZZ

Phew! The costumes have come!

COSTUMES

The Coolest Costume

Who has the coolest costume?

If you had a super-costume,
what would it look like?